NUTSHE⌐⌐
GROW
C⌐
& LIΓ⌐   ⌐⌐⌐

Everything you .. ⌐⌐q to know in a nutshell

Clive Simms

ALSO BY CLIVE SIMMS

Nutshell Guide to Growing Walnuts
Nutshell Guide to Growing Figs
Nutshell Guide to Growing Grapes

Published by:
Orchard House Books,
Woodhurst, Essendine,
Stamford, Lincs. PE9 4LQ
Tel: 01780 755615

ORCHARD HOUSE BOOKS

www.orchardhousebooks.com

ISBN 0-9544607-3-1

Contents

Introduction

Blueberries, cranberries and lingonberries are all species of *Vaccinium* grown both for their tasty fruit and ornamental qualities.

The American highbush blueberry (*Vaccinium corymbosum*) produces the berries that are available in shops and supermarkets. It's an easily grown deciduous shrub, 1.25m to 2m high, with pinkish white flowers, blue berries and leaves that develop red autumn tints.

American lowbush blueberries (*Vaccinium angustifolium & myrtilloides*) are rarely grown or sold here. However, they've been crossed with the highbush type to develop **half-high** blueberry plants that are compact, high yielding, and available in the UK.

The cranberry is a prostrate evergreen sub-shrub with trailing wiry stems and small  shiny leaves. The red fruit is around the size of a marble (1cm to 2cm across) and may be round or slightly pear shaped. Although there is a native European cranberry it's the larger fruited American species (*Vaccinium macrocarpon*) that is commonly grown.

The lingonberry or mountain cranberry (*Vaccinium vitis-idaea*) is a low growing evergreen shrub, around 30cm in height, found in Europe and North America. It has pinkish white, bell shaped flowers and pea sized scarlet fruit. The berries are smaller than true cranberries but they have a sweeter and more aromatic taste.

An increasing body of research has shown that these fruits make a valuable addition to the diet. They contain many health-promoting substances that help combat age related problems, high cholesterol levels and even cancer. Amongst these are large amounts of vitamins, anti-oxidants and antibacterial agents.

Blueberries in particular have received a lot of publicity in this respect but all three make an extremely important contribution to human health when eaten regularly.

At present almost all the blueberries, cranberries and lingonberries eaten in Britain are imported and sold at a premium price. They can easily be grown here and most gardens have enough space to produce home grown crops of these tasty and nutritious berries. This allows them to be picked and eaten at the peak of perfection ... without incurring any polluting air miles!

Blueberry

Soil

The correct soil acidity is the single most important factor for success. Blueberries and other *Vaccinium* species are **ericaceous** plants and require a very **acid soil** containing plenty of organic matter.

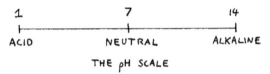

THE pH SCALE

Ideally, the pH of the soil should be between 4.0 and 5.0 for blueberries to thrive.

Soils that contain **lime** (calcium carbonate) are alkaline and the pH is too high for blueberries. If *Azaleas* and *Rhododendrons* don't succeed in your area it's very likely that your soil is also unsuitable for blueberries and most other species of *Vaccinium*. If there is any doubt check the soil with a soil pH meter obtainable from a garden centre. This will accurately measure the acidity or alkalinity (pH) of your soil.

If you intend to grow only one or two blueberries you can overcome the problem of unsuitable soil by growing plants in large pots or tubs filled with ericaceous compost. Another idea is to simply plant directly into a bale of acid moss peat in a similar way to growing tomatoes in a gro-bag. The bale can be free standing or buried… but remember to poke drainage holes into the bale first!

If you prefer to plant directly into soil that lacks the required acidity you'll need to correct the soil's pH first. Adding moss peat will increase the acidity of the soil a little, which may be enough for your situation.

Check that it says ericaceous on the pack as some peat has lime added to make it neutral.

If you need to achieve a greater pH change then you will have to add acidifying agents to the soil. The two most commonly used are **sulphur** and **aluminium sulphate**.

- **Sulphur** used at the rate of $38g/m^2$ will reduce the pH of a light sandy soil by one unit, that is, a soil of pH 6.0 will go down to pH 5.0. Heavy soils will require two or three times this amount of sulphur. As it takes time for the acidifying effect to take place add the sulphur the year before you intend to plant on the site.

- **Aluminium sulphate** used at six times the rate given for sulphur will give an immediate pH change of one unit. It's advisable to carry out this operation before planting.

The soil will have to be retreated from time to time as groundwater from the surrounding untreated soil eventually reasserts its natural pH. When adding these substances take care to avoid overdoing things, particularly with aluminium sulphate. Add this in several small applications and recheck the pH each time. In the event of making the soil too acid add garden lime to correct it.

A more permanent solution is to isolate the growing area from the surrounding soil. This may be done in two ways:

1. **Dig out** the planting site to a depth of 50cm and lay an impermeable membrane of heavy-duty plastic sheet before backfilling.

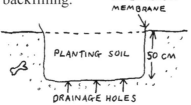

The sheet needs to cover both the floor and walls of the pit and must be punctured on the bottom to allow drainage. The backfilled soil may then be acidified as detailed on page 10.

2. **Construct a raised bed** using masonry blocks or old wooden railway sleepers to build an enclosure with 50cm high walls. The interior is then lined with a heavy-duty plastic sheet (with drainage holes), back filled, and the soil brought to the required acidity.

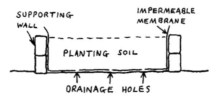

A raised bed is particularly useful on clay soil where drainage is poor as it avoids water-logging and minimises the extent to which alkaline ground water can leach back into your acidified soil.

Site & planting

The ideal site for blueberries is an open sheltered area which isn't prone to late spring frosts that may damage the flowers. Plants will tolerate a little shade but heavy shade is not suitable for them. The soil should be moisture retentive but well drained and not waterlogged.

Space bushes 1.5m apart in the row, with a 2m gap between rows. They're shallow rooted so don't plant too deeply. Let the soil mark on the stem of the plant be your guide.

 Being shallow rooted means they're vulnerable to weeds competing for water and nutrients so keep a clear weed free area of about 1.25m around the base of each bush. Over enthusiastic hoeing can cause root damage, so hand weeding is safer.

Feeding & watering

Blueberries form a symbiotic association with fungi in the soil and without it the plants will sicken and die. As these fungi thrive in soil rich in organic matter it makes sense to encourage them by feeding the soil with compost or leaf mould. Adding organic matter also helps keep the soil moist, which blueberries appreciate.

They respond well to an early spring feed of $65g/m^2$ of a chalk/lime free compound fertiliser such as John Innes base fertiliser or a general fertiliser labelled for 'acid loving

plants'. Follow this in April with 30g/m^2 of
ammonium sulphate. The latter
is a good source of nitrogen for
blueberries as it also helps to
acidify the soil, something that
nitrates don't do.

Blueberries require a steady supply of water
throughout the growing season so should be
irrigated during any dry spells. The **tap
water** in many areas is too 'hard' for
blueberries as it contains dissolved lime that
makes it alkaline. A clear indication of this is
your kettle furring up with lime scale. If you
have hard water you will need to collect
rainwater for your blueberry plants. The
'soft' water produced by domestic water
softeners that use common salt isn't suitable
for this purpose as it contains high levels of
sodium that may harm the plants.

If ericaceous plants are grown in soil that
lacks acidity, or are watered with 'hard'

water containing lime, the new leaves will turn yellow but retain prominent green veins. The condition is due to a lack of iron and is called **lime induced chlorosis**. It is caused by the high soil pH making iron unavailable to the plant in adequate amounts. As iron is required to make chlorophyll the new leaves lack this green pigment and become yellow… or even white in extreme cases.

Adding inorganic iron salts to the soil is unlikely to help as this also quickly becomes unavailable. The best remedy for this problem is to treat plants with **sequestered** or **chelated** iron obtainable from garden centres. This may be sprayed onto the leaves for a quick fix or used in the irrigation water. Iron in this form is unaffected by the soil's pH and will correct the deficiency. However, this is best viewed as a temporary solution; the long-term remedy is to attend to the underlying problem of the pH of the soil and/or irrigation water.

Pollination

Blueberries flower in April/May and the scented white flowers are attractive to many insects. Bees seem to be particularly fond of them.

Although a single blueberry plant will produce fruit, cropping is much heavier if cross-pollination takes place. If you have space, plant two or more unrelated cultivars of blueberry alongside one another or at least within 6m.

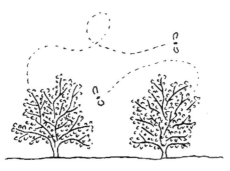

Pruning

It's prudent to remove all flower buds from young plants to enable the development of a sturdy framework of shoots and branches before allowing cropping to begin. The flower buds may be recognised as the fat buds towards the ends of the young shoots. After a couple of years allow flowering to take place and fruit to develop.

Pruning blueberries is similar to pruning blackcurrants. Both bear most of their fruit on young vigorous shoots so it's important to maintain a

← CUT HERE

CUT HERE ↗

supply of new stems from the base of the

plant by removing some of the old wood each winter.

After about four or five years the old woody branches tend to become less productive and should be completely pruned down to ground level to encourage new, more fruitful, growth.

However, take care not to overdo things and only remove a couple of branches each year or you can inadvertently cut away most of the flowering shoots completely!

In addition, any unproductive twiggy growth should be removed when winter pruning, together with low branches where the fruit is spoiled by rain splashing soil onto it.

Propagation

Plants raised from seeds are likely to be very variable and may prove to be disappointing as fruiting plants. The best method of propagating blueberries is by cuttings taken from named cultivars known to be heavy cropping.

Take 5cm to 10cm cuttings of young shoots in early July. Remove the lower leaves but retain several at the tip. Dip in hormone rooting powder and insert into rooting compost.

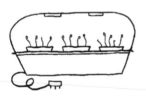 If kept at 20°C in a heated propagator they should root within a month or so. They should then be potted up and grown on for a year before planting in their final position.

Pests & diseases

There are only two likely problems when growing blueberries in Britain:

Birds: Netting is the best protection. A purpose made fruit cage is excellent, but a temporary structure made of strong canes or hoops of plastic water pipe will suffice.

Grey mould (*Botrytis cinerea*): The grey fungal growth may infect the fruit and can spread into the branches causing die-back. Combat this by immediately pruning any dead or diseased wood back to sound healthy tissue.

Harvesting

The fruit doesn't usually ripen all at once so bushes need to be picked several times over a period of about a month. Early ripening cultivars are ready in August while late ripening ones take until October.

Don't pick blueberries as soon as they turn blue, they develop a more intense flavour if left a few days longer to ripen fully. They'll also soften, develop a conspicuous white bloom on the skin, and be ready to fall into your hand with only the slightest encouragement. A berry rake (see page 32) is a good idea if there's lots of fruit to pick.

Freshly picked blueberries are delicious and will keep in a cool place for a week or so. They freeze well, make excellent juice and cheesecake… as well as the famed blueberry pie!

Cranberry & Lingonberry

Site, soil & planting

Cranberries require a sunny open site and moist acidic peaty soil. They're somewhat more tolerant of higher pH values (see page 8) than many species of *Vaccinium* but soil above pH 6.0 will cause problems.

A poor sandy acidic soil (pH 4.0 - 5.0) containing peat is ideal for the lingonberry. It requires drier conditions than the cranberry and will also tolerate more shading. However, shade depresses flowering and fruiting so an open sunny site is best to maximize your crop.

If your soil hasn't got the required acidity then amend it or construct a special growing area in the same way as detailed for blueberries (pages 9 -12). Both species are shallow rooted so don't require a great depth of soil, something around 8cm to 10cm is sufficient.

Alternatively, they may be grown in containers of ericaceous compost provided attention is given to ensuring the water quality is correct for acid loving plants (see pages 15 & 16).

Cranberry plants should be initially spaced around 45cm apart in the bed. In time they'll colonise all the available space, often rooting where the stems touch the soil. In the garden they could be used as an evergreen groundcover. The ground should be thoroughly prepared and be completely free of perennial weeds before planting. Make sure you remove annual weeds promptly.

Lingonberry beds initially have plants spaced 30cm to 45cm apart. They spread slowly by underground shoots and eventually join together to form extensive mats of growth.

Feeding & watering

Both cranberries and lingonberries are adapted to growing in soils very low in mineral nutrients and often succeed with very little feeding at all. However, if growth and cropping are poor a spring feed of nitrogen will help. Ammonium sulphate or urea are better than nitrates for this purpose. Take care when feeding as both may react badly to excessive amounts of nutrients. A pinch per plant is about right.

Cranberries require a constantly moist soil, but shouldn't be permanently submerged in water. The lingonberry grows better in drier soils, although some irrigation may be necessary during the summer months. Both should be watered with rainwater and not hard tap water.

Pollination

All cranberry plants are self-fertile so a single plant will produce fruit. Some, but not all, lingonberry plants are self-fertile and those that aren't need to be grown with a pollinating partner.

Even self-fertile cranberry and lingonberry cultivars crop more heavily if cross-pollination takes place so wherever possible plant more than one cultivar. However, cranberries won't pollinate lingonberries and vice versa.

Some lingonberry cultivars flower twice a year in both spring and autumn. The scarlet berries against the second flush of pinkish white blossom makes a pleasing sight.

Pruning & propagation

No pruning is necessary for cranberries apart from trimming off any straggly vertical growth with shears.

Lingonberries also require minimal annual pruning but benefit by being cut or mowed down to ground level every two or three years. This re-invigorates the plants to produce fruitful new growth.

The cranberry is easily propagated by layering or cuttings. Layering is simple and only requires the prostrate stem to be pegged down to the soil. After a year or so the stem may be detached from the main plant and the rooted part planted in its new situation.

PIN DOWN STEM
WITH WIRE LOOP

Cranberry cuttings are successful at almost any time of year. Treat early summer softwood cuttings with rooting hormone and keep in a humid atmosphere. Winter cuttings of 10cm long sections of stem may be placed in pots without further attention, or directly into their final position and allowed to root there. It's a good idea to place two or three cuttings together to allow for the odd failure.

Lingonberry cuttings may be taken in late June/early July but if only a few plants are required it's easier to simply detach rooted shoots from the edge of an established plant.

Pests & diseases

Like blueberries, one of the joys of growing cranberries and lingonberries is that neither are bothered by any major pests and diseases when grown in the UK.

Occasional minor infestations of **aphids** and **scale insect** may be encountered. These can be dealt with by spraying with an appropriate insecticide… or even picking the pests off by hand if only a few plants are being grown.

Some lingonberries are susceptible to the **fungal root disease** *Phytophthora* when grown on poorly drained sites and may decline and die very quickly. Improving drainage or replanting with more resistant plants should solve the problem.

Birds usually only eat cranberries and lingonberries when food is short in winter.

Harvesting

Both cranberries and lingonberries ripen in late autumn when the fruit turns red and is easy to detach from the plant. The flavour improves if harvesting is left until after the first frosts of winter. Both fruits hang well on the plant if harvesting is delayed.

Ripe cranberries will bounce when dropped, hence the alternative common name of 'bounceberry'.

On a domestic scale cranberries can be picked by hand but lingonberries, being smaller, can be tedious to harvest in this way. Berry rakes are commonly used to harvest small berries in the USA and Scandinavia, but they're rarely sold here. You can make one by cutting teeth into a dustpan.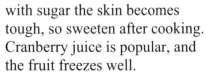

Cranberries are traditionally used to make cranberry sauce but they're also suitable for tarts, pies, crumbles and cakes. When cooked with sugar the skin becomes tough, so sweeten after cooking. Cranberry juice is popular, and the fruit freezes well.

Lingonberries keep for several weeks in a fridge, and several years in a freezer. They're less acidic and richer in flavour than cranberries, but are used in the same way.

Both cranberries and lingonberries are high in vitamin C and also contain large amounts of benzoic acid, a natural preservative, plus anthocyanin antioxidants similar to those found in blueberries.

Buying your plant

There are many cultivars of blueberry, cranberry and lingonberry to choose from. Be aware that smaller fruit often has a more intense flavour. Bigger is not always better… particularly with blueberries!

Most garden centres or nurseries are likely to have only a limited range of these plants. For a greater choice consult the **RHS Plant Finder** to see who supplies the cultivar you require. There's also an internet version at **www.rhs.org.uk**.

Some excellent cultivars are available in Europe but are not yet sold in the UK. However, if a commercial supplier can be found within the European Union it should be possible to import them without too much trouble.

BLUEBERRIES

Bluecrop: Highbush type. Ripens mid season. Large fruit. Heavy cropper. Good autumn colour.

Bluetta: Highbush type. Ripens early. Medium sized fruit. Heavy cropper. Compact bush with good autumn colour.

Darrow: Highbush type. Ripens late. Large fruit. Heavy cropper.

Jersey: Highbush type. Ripens late. Medium sized fruit. Moderately productive.

Northland: Half-high type. Ripens early. Small well flavoured fruit. Heavy cropper. Good autumn colour.

Patriot: Highbush type. Ripens early. Large fruit. Heavy cropper. Low growing.

Pütte: Lowbush type. 20cm to 35cm tall. Ripens mid season. Medium sized fruit. Very productive. Swedish.

Top Hat: Lowbush type. Ripens mid season. Medium sized, good quality fruit. Compact and attractive, growing to 50cm high by 60cm wide. Excellent for containers.

CRANBERRIES

CN: Fruit large. Moderate cropper.

Early Black: Fruit small/medium, dark red/black. Ripens early. Low yielding.

Franklin: Fruit medium/large, dark red. Ripens early and keeps well.

Olson's Honkers: Fruit very large.

Pilgrim: Fruit large, red with yellow undercolour. Very productive.

LINGONBERRIES

Erntedank, **Erntekrone** & **Erntesegen**: All are good cultivars from Germany.

Ida: 30cm to 40cm tall. Very large fruit, up to 5g per berry in weight. Swedish.

Koralle: 30cm to 40cm tall, spreading habit. Self-fertile. Medium/large fruit. *Phytopthora* susceptible. Flowers twice per year.

Red Pearl: 30cm to 50cm tall, spreading habit. Productive. Medium/large fruit. Disease resistant. Flowers twice per year.

Sanna: 15cm to 30cm tall, erect habit. Slow growing but very productive. Large fruit. Disease resistant. Swedish.

Sussi: 10cm to 20cm tall, spreading habit. Slow growing but productive. Large fruit. Disease resistant. Swedish.